J. WESTON
WALCH
PUBLISHER

MW00343900

test time!

Critical Reading

PRACTICE BOOKS THAT MEET THE STANDARDS

2145 S. Chelton Road
Colorado Springs, CO 80916

DATE DUE	

User's Guide
to
Walch Reproducible Books

Purchasers of this book are granted the right to reproduce all pages.

This permission is limited to a single teacher, for classroom use only.

Any questions regarding this policy or requests to purchase further reproduction rights should be addressed to

Permissions Editor
J. Weston Walch, Publisher
321 Valley Street • P.O. Box 658
Portland, Maine 04104-0658

Colorado Middle School
2145 S. Chelton Road
Colorado Springs, CO 80916

1   2   3   4   5   6   7   8   9   10
ISBN 0-8251-4478-7

Copyright © 2003
J. Weston Walch, Publisher
P.O. Box 658 • Portland, Maine 04104-0658
www.walch.com

Printed in the United States of America

table of contents

Test Your Best!

We all have to take tests. Often, our abilities are measured by how well we test. Each year, more and more tests are added to our lives. District, state, and national assessments reflect student progress, teacher abilities, administrative skills, and curriculum standards. In other words, a lot is riding on these tests. It is important for you to take them seriously, just as your superintendent, your principal, and your teachers do.

The books in the *Test Time!* series were designed to help you practice your test-taking skills. They also provide you with successful strategies and tips to follow at test time. As you well know, practice makes perfect. The more you practice, the higher you score. When you do well, not only are you successful, but your teachers, your administrators, and your state legislators are, too. This means that they took the testing seriously and wanted to help you be successful. It's a team effort.

With all that in mind, be confident that you can succeed. You have the power; now just practice the skills. Good luck!

Even when you're not in a testing situation, it's important to understand what you read. When you *are* taking a test, though, it's even more critical that you really "get" what each reading passage is all about. Here are some reminders that can boost your comprehension.

Understanding Directions

Usually, the very first kind of reading you come to in a test are the **directions.** As everybody knows, the directions tell you what to do—and they all look pretty much the same on reading tests, don't they?

No. In fact, even within one test there are often multiple sets of directions, and each one may be just a bit different from the others. So, **read all directions carefully.** Sometimes they contain important clues about the passage you are about to read; sometimes they tell you to mark an answer choice in a special way. Don't skip this important step!

Understanding a Reading Passage

WHAT KIND OF WRITING *IS* THIS?

After you read the directions on a test, you'll come to a reading passage. What do you do? Even before you plunge into the reading, you should **skim the passage** to determine what **genre,** or basic type, of writing it is. Here are some of the most common types of writing:

- **fiction**—an invented work; part of a novel or short story, for example

- **nonfiction**—not fiction; part of a book or an article, or an essay or editorial

- **poetry**—all kinds—rhyming, nonrhyming, very short or very long

- reading passage with a **graphic** to interpret—chart, table, graph, map, photo, or drawing

Look for key names, dates, areas of conversation (if any), sections that appear to have a lot of detail, charts, pictures, and so on. Also, scan for the **main idea.** With longer passages, scan for the **topic sentence** in each paragraph. (Remember: Topic sentences often come at the beginning of a paragraph, but they can also be found elsewhere.)

Now Read It!

Once you have oriented yourself and you have decided what type of writing it is, go ahead and read the passage. **Read carefully but smoothly:** Don't get hung up on every single vocabulary word you don't know. Don't try to memorize each detail. Just read through the selection and focus on understanding the **main points.** You can always go back if you need to. For now, you are looking for the big picture.

As soon as you have finished reading, **stop** for one moment and **reflect:** "What message is this author really trying to get across?"

Map out Longer Passages in Your Head

For longer reading selections, try to make a mental map of each paragraph and what it contains. Keep in mind the placement of key paragraphs—ones that contain important details, for example—so that you can easily find them again later if you need to.

Understanding the Author's Techniques and Purpose

Careful reading includes recognizing an author's style, tone, and reasons (or purpose) for writing a particular passage. Watch for these as you read so that you can have the fullest comprehension of the passage.

Style

Style involves an author's own special way of using language. Some authors create long, complex sentences with many descriptive phrases. Others write short, bare-bones sentences that require the reader to read between the lines. *Think* about the ways in which the author chooses words and puts sentences together. Once you have a handle on this, you'll read the passage more quickly, and your comprehension will increase.

TONE

Look for words and phrases in a reading passage that help create an overall feeling. How does the author *sound?* Every writer has a certain attitude toward his or her subject; this attitude is expressed in the author's choice of words. The tone of a reading passage can be approving or critical, impersonal or passionate, pleading or proud, skeptical or enthusiastic. Or, it might reflect another feeling altogether. *Be aware of the author's tone* as you read in order to fully appreciate the meaning of the passage.

PURPOSE

Every author writes for a reason. Certainly, most authors write to share information that they feel is interesting or important. However, each individual author writes with a slightly different audience in mind, and with a slightly different goal. This is the author's *purpose.* Readers who understand *why* an author is writing will be more aware of the ways in which the author tries to persuade them to think about the subject in a certain way.

Here are some of the most common purposes for writing:

- to **entertain** (to amuse, frighten, enchant, or otherwise give the reader pleasure)
- to **inform** (to tell about something the reader has not known before)
- to **persuade** (to try to convince the reader to do or think something)
- to **argue** (to disagree with another point of view)
- to **illustrate a point**

Understanding Questions

WHAT TYPE OF QUESTION IS THIS?

Now for the test questions! Remember that test questions usually fall into just a handful of categories. If you understand what category a question belongs to, you will most likely find the correct answer more easily. On pages 4 to 6 are some of the most common question types.

Basic Comprehension

These questions are designed to see how well you have understood the main facts or events in the passage you have just read. Basic comprehension questions are generally the easiest kinds of questions to answer. If you don't immediately know the correct response, you can go back to the passage and find it without much trouble.

Example: How many miles did Sonia have to run in the charity race?

  A. 3

  B. 3.5

  C. 4

  D. 4.5

Answer: B

Most of the simplest questions on a test fall into the basic comprehension category, including questions about vocabulary and parts of speech.

Main Idea Versus Details

These questions ask you to do some extra thinking. You must sort out all possible answers in your head, then decide which one answer BEST sums up the paragraph or passage.

Example: Which of the following best explains the main idea of this story?

  A. Jose couldn't sleep that night.

  B. Jose's mother said that he seemed very tense.

  C. Jose was so worried about his chemistry test that he had been a nervous wreck all week.

  D. At school, Jose's friend Carmen told him that he seemed distracted.

Answer: C

Inference

Inference questions ask you to use clues in the text to arrive at an answer that is never directly stated anywhere in the text. The answer to this type of question is only implied in the reading passage, but there should be enough information in the reading to help you make that mental leap.

Examples of inference questions:

- What is the most likely reason for Mr. Toshaka's absence?   OR

- What can we conclude about the fact that Mr. Toshaka has been away so long?   OR

- According to the information in this passage, Mr. Toshaka has probably been away because _____.

Fact Versus Opinion

Again, these questions make you do a little extra thinking. When you are asked to distinguish between facts and opinions, just remember to test each answer choice by asking yourself, "Can this be *proved*, or is there another possible way to look at it? Is there an acceptable argument against this statement?" If there is no other reasonable way to look at the statement, then it is a *fact*. If there is a way to argue with it, then it's an *opinion*.

Example: The following statements have been taken directly from the reading passage. Which one states an opinion rather than a fact?

A. The Boston Red Sox have lost the last three games they've played.

B. The Yankees won the pennant last year, and their manager hopes they'll do it again this year.

C. The Chicago Cubs hold the home-run record so far this season.

D. The Miami Dolphins are the most talented team in the league this year.

Answer: D

Negative Questions

Remember: **Any of the preceding question types described can also be asked in negative form.** It's important to watch for these and to react accordingly.

Examples of negative questions:

Basic comprehension: Captain Gomez put all of the following items into his pack *except* which one? OR

Which one of the following countries was *not* an Ally during World War II?

Main idea versus details: Which of the statements below does *not* reflect one of the details in this passage about the trans-continental railroad?

Inference: Which one of the assumptions below would you *not* make about the doctor in this story?

Fact versus opinion: All of the statements below *except one* are facts about the space shuttle. Which one of these statements is not a fact?

Understanding Answer Choices

Careful reading is the key to understanding the directions on a test. It is also key to understanding the reading passage itself, as well as the questions that follow. But, you can't stop there—you also have to **read each answer choice carefully,** too. Once you have read all of the answer choices, you can usually sort them out into various common categories:

- **impossible, or just too farfetched** (Sometimes these are even quite silly and are the easiest to eliminate.)

- **close but not quite**

- **in the text, but not relevant**

- **relevant, but not in the text**

- **too broad/too specific**

- **the correct answer** (By eliminating the other choices, you can now be sure that this is the answer you want.)

If you have eliminated one or more of the possible answers, but find that you're still having trouble choosing between two or three finalists, then go back to the reading for a quick refresher. If that doesn't help, carefully read the remaining choices once again. Perhaps you'll suddenly notice a key word that tells you an answer doesn't really "fit" after all.

* * * * *

If you follow all of the steps outlined in this section, then you'll be a more efficient and accurate reader—not just in testing situations, but in your other work, too.

test-taking words

The following section will help you look a little more closely at directions, questions, and answer choices on reading tests. You will learn to recognize some of the words and phrases that are used frequently in reading comprehension tests, and you'll learn how to respond to test questions more accurately as a result.

Word Signals in Directions and Questions

Simply by paying attention to the specific wording in test directions and test questions, you can often learn something about the kind of answer you should be selecting. Here is a very simple example:

> **Directions:** Read the passage below. Then answer each question that follows by marking the *best* possible choice.

Although this set of directions appears to be straightforward, you'll notice that one word is in italics—the word *best*. What does this mean? The italicized word is there for emphasis. The test writers wanted to be sure that you noticed it. Why? Maybe because you will be asked to choose between two (or even three) possible answers that are quite similar in meaning—or that both come close to answering the question correctly. This means that you will have to be especially careful when reading the answer choices. **Do not mark any answer as correct until you have carefully read every single choice.** There may be some answer choices that are meant to "trick" less careful readers.

Other words and phrases to look for in test directions and questions are listed below.

TERMS TO WATCH FOR IN DIRECTIONS

When you are instructed to keep an eye out for certain features or examples in a reading passage, you can be sure that one or more test questions will be focusing on them.

Term	Example in Test
be alert for/watch for	As you read the following passage, watch for examples that reveal the main character's personality.
be sure to	Be sure to watch for descriptive words and phrases as you read.
best/that *best* answers the question/ the *best* possible answer/ the *best* possible choice	Respond to the questions that follow by selecting the *best* possible answer.
keeping in mind	Read the passage that follows, keeping in mind the time in which it was written.

TERMS SIGNALING SPECIFIC QUESTION TYPES

Basic comprehension questions and fact/opinion questions are generally self-explanatory in terms of their wording on tests; they are, therefore, not given individual listings below.

Term	Example in Test
Main idea/detail questions	
What is the main idea?	What is the main idea expressed in this essay?
Which best sums up?	Which of the following statements best sums up the most important idea in this article?
summarize	How would you best summarize the feelings of Dr. Weisberg during her walk to the hospital?
supporting detail	Which of these statements is a main idea, not a supporting detail?
Inference questions	
Based on information in the [passage],	Based on information in this letter, what is the most likely reason for the submarine's disappearance?
conclude	What can the reader conclude about how the party turned out?
infer/inference	What can we infer from Katya's attitude toward Keisha?
	(continued)

(continued)

likely, most likely	What is the most likely reason for the failure of the cookie sale?
probable/probably	Judging from the reporter's comments, what is probably happening to the police detective at that moment?
seem to be saying	What does the author seem to be saying about how most people treat their pets?
Why do you think . . .?	Why do you think the author chose to include a reference to the Statue of Liberty in this passage?
Negative questions	
all but one	All but one of the following statements are true about Ms. Fillippo's vacation. Select the one that is untrue.
except	The narrator says all of these things about his friend Mica *except* _____.
not	Which of the following opinions about Los Angeles is *not* expressed by the writer of this editorial?

TERMS SIGNALING AUTHOR/WRITING-RELATED QUESTIONS

Term	Example in Test
attitude	The author's attitude toward air travel can best be described as _____.
mood	Which of the following most accurately describes the mood created by this poem?
point of view/viewpoint	From whose point of view is this story told?
purpose/intent/reason	What seems to have been the author's intent in writing this passage?
style	In one paragraph of four to five sentences, describe this author's style, providing specific examples from the story.
theme	Which of the following statements best summarizes the theme of this passage?

(continued)

(continued)	
tone	The tone of the editorial about city bus service is _____.
topic	What is the main topic of this article?
topic sentence	The topic sentence in paragraph 5 is which of the following?

Word Signals in Answer Choices

"EXTREME" TERMS

Words or phrases like those below *usually* indicate that the answer choice should be eliminated; however, read the answer choice carefully to double-check!

- absolutely
- always
- completely
- extremely
- never
- totally
- very

SECTION 1

SECTION 1.1

Directions: Read the passage below. Then answer each question that follows by selecting the *best* possible choice.

When spring came, after that hard winter, one could not get enough of the nimble air. Every morning I wakened with a fresh consciousness that winter was over. There were none of the signs of spring for which I used to watch in Virginia, no budding woods or blooming gardens. There was only spring itself; the throb of it, the light restlessness, the vital essence of it everywhere; in the sky, in the swift clouds, in the pale sunshine, and in the warm, high wind—rising suddenly, sinking suddenly, impulsive and playful like a big puppy that pawed you and then lay down to be petted. If I had been tossed down blindfold on that red prairie, I should have known that it was spring.

Everywhere now there was the smell of burning grass. Our neighbors burned off their pasture before the new grass made a start, so that the fresh growth would not be mixed with the dead stand of last year. Those light, swift fires, running about the country, seemed a part of the same kindling that was in the air.

—Willa Cather, *My Antonia*

1. What was the author's primary purpose in writing this selection?

   A. to tell a story

   B. to instruct or inform

   C. to state an opinion

   D. to ask a question

GO ON ▶

2. Which of the following sentences best summarizes this reading passage?

   A. Life in Virginia was happier for the narrator than life on the prairie.

   B. Spring is the loveliest season of the year.

   C. On the prairie, spring arrives with unmistakable signs.

   D. It was important to burn off the old grass before the new grass began to grow.

3. What is the meaning of *nimble* as it is used in line 2?

   A. having flexible joints

   B. fresh, lively

   C. sweet-smelling

   D. intelligent

4. The reference to the puppy in the first paragraph is an example of which of the following literary devices?

   A. metaphor

   B. simile

   C. onomatopoeia

   D. alliteration

5. Information in this passage suggests that which of the following statements is most likely true?

   A. The narrator does not really approve of his neighbors' burning the old grass.

   B. The narrator will soon be going back to Virginia.

   C. The narrator finds the seasons milder on the prairie than in Virginia.

   D. This is the first year that the narrator has spent in prairie country.

STOP

Directions: Read the passage below. Then answer each question that follows by selecting the *best* possible choice.

Instructions for Using Your New National Flag

Congratulations! You are now the owner of a high-quality flag that should bring enjoyment to you and your family for many years to come. The following instructions, based on international agreement regarding correct flag usage, will help ensure that you always display your flag in an appropriate manner.

1. Display your flag outdoors between sunrise and sunset. It may also be displayed at night if it is well illuminated. Do not fly your flag in poor weather.

2. Your flag should never be allowed to touch the floor, ground, or water. It should be hung aloft, with room to move freely in the air.

3. The national flag should never be hung below any other flag (state, provincial, county, civic, and so on) on a pole or staff. It takes priority over all other flags and should be flown in the topmost position. If flags of more than one nation are flying at the same time, each national flag should be flown from its own separate pole or staff. National flags should be arranged in alphabetical order according to the host country's official language.

4. In a ground-based lineup of either two or four flags, the national flag should always be placed at the observer's left. In a line of three flags, the national flag should be placed in the middle. In a line of five or more flags, *two* national flags should be used—one for each end of the line.

5. In a semicircle of flags, the national flag should appear in the exact center. In a full circle, the national flag should appear in the exact center *opposite from the main entrance or key observation point.*

6. As a sign of official mourning, the national flag may be flown at half-mast on a flagpole.

7. When your flag is no longer in good condition, it should be disposed of appropriately; this customarily involves burning the flag privately *in safe, controlled conditions.*

1. The general purpose of this reading selection is to _____.

   A. ask a question

   B. tell a story

   C. state an opinion

   D. instruct or inform

2. The word *illuminated* in item 1 means _____.

   A. lighted up

   B. well protected

   C. having great wisdom

   D. upright

3. The word *aloft* in item 2 means _____.

   A. from the roofline

   B. up in the air

   C. over the water

   D. proudly

4. According to this passage, if a national flag and a state flag are being flown at the same time, which of the following should occur?

   A. The state flag should be flown above the national flag.

   B. The state flag and the national flag should fly on separate poles.

   C. The national flag should be flown above the state flag.

   D. The flags should be displayed side by side.

5. Which of the following statements best expresses the main idea of this passage?

   A. One's national flag must always be handled with the utmost respect and displayed to its best advantage.

   B. There is a general international agreement about how to display flags in the most appropriate manner.

   C. Each nation on the earth, however small, has its own flag.

   D. The national flag should never be allowed to touch the ground or the water.

STOP

Directions: Read the passage below. Then answer each question that follows by selecting the *best* possible choice.

What is a *fresco?* Some of the most famous paintings in the world are frescoes. Yet, these special paintings are not found in picture frames, carefully arranged to hang on the walls of museums. In fact, a fresco is a very special type of painted wall or ceiling.

Wall paintings are often called *murals.* Murals, however, are not necessarily frescoes. How can the two be distinguished?

A mural can be painted directly onto the surface of a wall with oil, acrylic, or even watercolor paint. A mural can also first be painted onto canvas and then attached to a wall with glue. In both cases, the mural is a painting that lies on the outer surface of the wall.

A true fresco, on the other hand, is actually painted *into* the wall material itself. The fresco painter first prepares fresh plaster. A coat of the wet plaster is then applied to a section of wall or ceiling. The artist paints directly onto the plaster before it dries, using pure pigment (color). As the plaster dries, it absorbs the color and then hardens, providing an excellent "casing" for the artist's work.

The challenge for the fresco painter is to apply the color before the plaster dries too much, which can cause the pigment to powder or flake off at a later date. However, if the painter begins work too soon, the plaster may be too wet to absorb the pigment properly, which means that the color simply will not hold. Therefore, the fresco painter has only a few hours in which to apply the pigment so that it is properly absorbed a fraction of an inch below the plaster's surface.

Are frescoes durable? Of course, that depends on how well the buildings that house them are preserved. Heavy moisture, for example, can cause serious damage to these paintings. Under favorable conditions, though, a fresco will last for centuries. Just think of Michelangelo's splendid frescoes in the ceiling of the Vatican's Sistine Chapel. They were painted between 1508 and 1512, and—with the help of recent restoration—are still considered one of the wonders of Western art.

1. Which of the following statements is true about frescoes?

    A. *Fresco* is another term for *mural.*

    B. A fresco is an oil, an acrylic, or a watercolor painting applied to a wall or ceiling.

    C. The colors in a fresco are absorbed into the wall or ceiling material itself.

    D. A fresco is painted onto a smooth, dry plaster wall or ceiling.

2. The word *durable* means _____.

    A. long-lasting

    B. encased in a hard shell

    C. of great artistic importance

    D. expensive

3. According to this passage, fresco painting is especially challenging because _____.

    A. the artist has limited time to apply the pigment before the plaster dries

    B. walls and ceilings are usually too large for artists to paint well

    C. wet plaster is very heavy and difficult for the artist to make smooth

    D. the pigment colors fade so quickly

4. When did Michelangelo paint his famous frescoes in the Sistine Chapel?

    A. in the early fifteenth century

    B. in the late fifteenth century

    C. in the early sixteenth century

    D. in the late sixteenth century

5. Information in this passage suggests that _____.

    A. frescoes are harder to see than other paintings because they are below the surface of the wall or ceiling

    B. frescoes are considered more beautiful than other kinds of painting

    C. most frescoes were painted in the 1500s

    D. frescoes are very sensitive to the climate and environment in which they are painted

STOP

SECTION 2.1

Directions: Carefully read this passage. A number of questions will follow that relate to the passage. Answer each question by selecting the *best* possible choice.

1   Although she later became known for her writings about the sea, Rachel Carson was born in 1907 far from the coast, in the hill country of western Pennsylvania. She grew up in a simple farmhouse, learning about the world of nature—particularly local bird life—under her mother's enthusiastic guidance.

2   The youngest of three children, Rachel was a quiet, shy child who spent much of her time reading and writing. At the age of ten, she was thrilled to see one of her own poems published in *Saint Nicholas,* a popular children's magazine of the time. Throughout her school and college years, Rachel continued to write and to submit her work to publishers.

3   In 1925, Rachel Carson entered the Pennsylvania College for Women (now Chatham College) on a four-year scholarship. While there, she was awarded a summer-study fellowship at the Marine Biological Laboratory in Woods Hole, Massachusetts. This first trip to the East Coast gave rise to Carson's lifelong love of the ocean and all the life forms it harbored. "To stand at the edge of the sea," she said, ". . . is to have knowledge of things that are as eternal as any earthly life can be."

4   Carson graduated from college with honors in 1929. She then went to Johns Hopkins University in Baltimore, Maryland, to do graduate work in marine biology. Awarded a master's degree in zoology in 1932, she spent the next few years teaching part time at the university.

5   Carson's professional life changed in 1935, when she was hired by the United States Bureau of Fisheries (later known as the U.S. Fish and Wildlife Service). She began on a part-time basis, writing radio scripts about science for a show called *Romance Under the Waters.* In 1936, Carson became the first woman to pass the federal civil service examination. She was then hired full time by the Bureau, where her career advanced steadily. For the next seventeen years, she worked there as a well-respected scientist and editor.

GO ON ▶

6   Urged on by a colleague who thought very highly of her writing, Carson sent one of her articles off to the *Atlantic Monthly* in 1937. The magazine responded by publishing the article, titled "Undersea." Encouraged, Carson eventually turned the article into a full-fledged book, published in 1941 as *Under the Sea-Wind*. Although it did not receive much public attention, this first book remained Carson's personal favorite.

7   Over the next decade, Carson continued to work and write. Then, in 1951, her second book was published. Called *The Sea Around Us*, this beautifully written work about the nature of the ocean made Rachel Carson famous. *The Sea Around Us* won the National Book Award and was on the *New York Times* best-seller list for more than a year and a half.

8   With the money from her book sales, Carson was able to leave her government job in 1952. She turned her attention to full-time writing, using her newly purchased summer house on the coast of Maine to further explore the sea and its shore. The result was the book that Carson most enjoyed writing: *The Edge of the Sea*, published in 1955. This third book about the ocean increased her fame as a naturalist and writer.

9   The late 1950s brought a change in focus. Like some other scientists, Carson knew that the government was promoting the use of pesticides, including DDT. These chemicals were designed to kill the insects and other pests that damaged farm crops and spread disease. However, Carson was convinced that such poisons were also deadly to many harmless species, and would eventually cause great damage to the earth. She decided that she must make the public more aware of these dangers. "The more I learned about pesticides, the more appalled I became," she said. "I realized that here was the material for a book. What I discovered was that everything that meant most to me as a naturalist was being threatened, and that nothing I could do would be more important."

10   The result was Carson's best-known book, *Silent Spring*. Published in 1962, it created such a stir that even President Kennedy was persuaded to order more careful testing of pesticides. Carson was also asked to testify before Congress in 1963 about the dangers of these chemicals. She took the opportunity to press Congress for new laws to protect the environment.

11   After a long battle with cancer, Rachel Carson died in 1964. This gifted scientist and poet had spent her life making the world more aware of the lovely—yet fragile—natural world around us and how the human race must cherish and protect it.

GO ON ▶

1. What genre (type of writing) does this passage represent?

   A. short story

   B. fable

   C. autobiography

   D. biography

2. What was the author's main purpose in writing the passage?

   A. to entertain

   B. to inform

   C. to persuade

   D. to give directions

3. Rachel Carson spent much of her early days doing which of the following?

   A. farming with her mother

   B. raising chickens with her siblings

   C. reading and writing

   D. walking on the seashore

4. When did Carson first see the Atlantic Ocean?

   A. at the age of ten, when her first poem was published

   B. during a summer in Massachusetts when she was a college student

   C. when she bought a summer house in Maine

   D. when she was a graduate student at Johns Hopkins University

5. Rachel Carson was the first woman to do which of the following?

   A. have an article published in the *Atlantic Monthly*

   B. testify before Congress

   C. work at the Marine Biological Laboratory in Woods Hole

   D. pass the civil service exam

6. In the sixth paragraph, what does the word *eventually* mean?

   A. at a later time

   B. as a major event

   C. solemnly

   D. with great happiness

GO ON ▶

7. In the ninth paragraph, what is the meaning of the word *appalled*?

   A. shocked

   B. attracted to something or someone

   C. growing bored

   D. following a rule or law

8. How old was Rachel Carson when she died?

   A. sixty-three

   B. fifty-three

   C. sixty-seven

   D. fifty-seven

9. It is likely that Carson enjoyed writing *The Edge of the Sea* most of all her books because

   A. it was on the *New York Times* best-seller list for more than eighteen months.

   B. it was her third book about ocean life.

   C. she no longer had to hold down a full-time job while trying to write.

   D. she had so much help from coworkers in writing the book.

10. Each of the following statements appears in the reading about Rachel Carson. Which statement best summarizes the main idea of the passage?

   A. Although she later became known for her writings about the sea, Rachel Carson was born in 1907 far from the coast, in the hill country of western Pennsylvania.

   B. Called *The Sea Around Us,* this beautifully written work about the nature of the ocean made Rachel Carson famous.

   C. This gifted scientist and poet had spent her life making the world more aware of the lovely—yet fragile—natural world around us and how the human race must cherish and protect it.

   D. She turned her attention to full-time writing, using her newly purchased summer house on the coast of Maine to further explore the sea and its shore.

STOP

Directions: Read the poem below. Then answer the questions that follow.

The Pines

Throughout the soft and sunlit day
The pennoned* pines, in strict array,
Stand grim and silent, gaunt and gray.

But when the blasts of winter keen,**
They whisper each to each, and lean
Like comrades with a bond between.

And seeing them deport them so,
One almost thinks they seek to show
How mortal-like mere trees may grow.

For men, in peace time, stand aloof,
One from the other, asking proof,
Of lineage and race and roof.

But let the blast of battle call,—
Lo! they're unquestioning comrades all,
Who side by side will stand or fall.

—Julie Mathilde Lippman

*pennoned = shaped like a long, triangular flag or wing
**keen = make a mournful noise

1. Which literary device is used more than once in the first stanza?

   A. alliteration

   B. onomatopoeia

   C. simile

   D. hyperbole

GO ON ▶

2. Which two literary devices does the poet use in lines 2 and 3 of the second stanza?

    A. irony and metaphor

    B. irony and simile

    C. personification and onomatopoeia

    D. simile and personification

3. What does the poet's main point seem to be in the fourth stanza?

    A. In times of peace, men are always in such a hurry that they appear to be in a race.

    B. Anyone who builds a house wants to see proof that the roof is of the highest quality.

    C. Human beings are peace-loving creatures who usually don't seem very interested in the world around them.

    D. Human beings tend to be snobs, avoiding friendships with other people unless they are social "equals."

4. Which of the following statements best summarizes the theme of this poem?

    A. The pines are grim-looking trees, especially in the winter; they resemble men who are standing up in a line, facing the cold wind.

    B. Men are too busy with their own affairs to notice the simple beauties of nature, like the tall pines that shelter us from the cold winds.

    C. The pine trees resemble human beings; in quiet times, they seem indifferent to each other, but in stormy times they lean together for mutual support.

    D. When pine trees are damaged by the winter weather, they tend to fall down together in one long line.

5. **Short-answer response:** In a few sentences, describe the mood of *The Pines*. What specific feelings does the poem bring to mind?

_____

_____

_____

_____

_____

_____

_____

Directions: The poem below was composed and sung by Chinese immigrants who had come to America in the 1800s to work on the transcontinental railroad. Read the poem. Then answer the questions that follow.

A Gust of Fall Wind

A gust of fall wind blowing cold;
A fall of white dew turned to frost.
The cruel frost freezes each blade of grass,
And the grasshopper dies in his grassy nest.
—Traditional

1. This poem contains several effective examples of _____.

   A. onomatopoeia

   B. repetition

   C. simile

   D. alliteration

2. What is the overall mood of the poem?

   A. bleak and sad

   B. angry and sarcastic

   C. humorous

   D. hopeful

3. How does the poet use personification to emphasize the theme?

   A. The frost is described as "cruel," which is a human characteristic, to stress the harshness of the winter.

   B. The poet includes a reference to a grasshopper, which is a living thing.

   C. The "fall of white dew" turning to frost refers to death.

   D. The reference to "each blade of grass" being frozen makes the reader think of human beings who are cold in the wintertime.

GO ON ▶

4. The poet probably mentions the grasshopper and its nest for all of the following reasons *except* _____.

A. the grasshopper is a metaphor for a human being—like one of the Chinese railroad workers—who is facing the harsh winter weather

B. the grasshopper's "grassy nest" makes the reader think of a warm, cozy, safe place to live, which ends up being crushed by the cold, "cruel" environment

C. grasshoppers, like the one in this poem, can sometimes eat farm crops and should therefore be eliminated before they can do too much damage

D. like the railroad workers themselves, the grasshopper is a very small, fragile creature in the midst of an uncaring, sometimes brutal, world

5. **Short-answer response:** In one brief paragraph (four to five complete sentences), compare "The Pines" (Section 2.2) with "A Gust of Fall Wind" (Section 2.3). Giving examples to back up your thinking, explain how the two poems are different in terms of the following: theme, tone/mood, type of verse (meter, rhyme, and so on), and literary devices.

_____

_____

_____

_____

_____

_____

_____

_____

_____

_____

_____

_____

_____

_____

_____

STOP

SECTION 3.1

Directions: Read the newspaper editorial below. Then respond to each of the questions that follow by selecting the one *best* answer.

1   Our apologies to all the teachers out there, but it's time to pull the plug on homework. Today's students—especially high-school students—are doing too much of it, and it's causing nothing but stress in their lives. In fact, homework may even be causing some kids to drop out of school. How "educational" is that?

2   The American Association of Pediatrics recommends that the average high-school student get 9 hours of sleep per night. That sounds reasonable enough, yet it's often impossible to achieve. Consider this: Statistics from the Department of Health show that most high-school-age children wake up between 6:00 and 6:30 A.M. in order to get to school on time. This means that, in order to get the recommended 9 hours of sleep time in at night, those kids should be going to bed—with lights off—between 9:00 and 9:30 P.M. How often does that happen? With after-school sports, part-time jobs, family responsibilities, and 2 or 3 hours of *homework* every night (sometimes more), we'll wager that most sixteen- to eighteen-year-olds are actually getting to bed a whole lot later. This means that the average high-school student is almost always tired—and not working up to his or her potential.

3   The situation is even worse for students from low-income families. A recent study by the State Department of Education asked high-school dropouts if any *one factor* had played a key role in causing them to leave school. One hundred percent of the teenagers surveyed in this study mentioned homework as a "major problem." With very little help from the adults in their lives, and coping with poor housing conditions, these teens felt overwhelmed. The homework load seemed impossible to keep up with, and they fell further and further behind—until dropping out seemed to be the only solution.

4   Let's give all of our children a break. If teachers and parents can agree to less homework every night, then we'll have a happier, healthier student population, and more of them will be staying in school until graduation day.

1. The preceding passage was written primarily to do which of the following?

   A. entertain

   B. instruct

   C. give directions

   D. tell a story

   E. persuade

2. At the end of the second paragraph, the word *potential* means _____.

   A. being in peak physical condition

   B. being an honors student

   C. following the rules

   D. what someone is capable of achieving

   E. a strong drink

3. In the first paragraph, what part of speech is the word *stress?*

   A. noun

   B. verb

   C. adjective

   D. adverb

   E. conjunction

4. In the third paragraph, what part of speech is the word *overwhelmed?*

   A. noun

   B. verb

   C. adjective

   D. adverb

   E. conjunction

GO ON

5. The following statements have been taken from the passage on page 27. One statement is an opinion; the rest are facts. Which statement is the opinion?

A. The American Association of Pediatrics recommends that the average high-school student get 9 hours of sleep per night.

B. With after-school sports, part-time jobs, family responsibilities, and 2 or 3 hours of *homework* every night (sometimes more), we'll wager that most sixteen- to eighteen-year-olds are actually getting to bed a whole lot later.

C. Statistics from the Department of Health show that most high-school-age children wake up between 6:00 and 6:30 A.M. in order to get to school on time.

D. A recent study by the State Department of Education asked high-school dropouts if any *one factor* had played a key role in causing them to leave school.

E. One hundred percent of the teenagers surveyed in this study mentioned homework as a "major problem."

6. The following statements have been taken from the passage on page 27. One statement tells the main idea; the rest are details. Which statement is the main idea?

A. This means that, in order to get the recommended 9 hours of sleep time in at night, those kids should be going to bed—with lights off—between 9:00 and 9:30 P.M.

B. The homework load seemed impossible to keep up with, and they fell further and further behind—until dropping out seemed to be the only solution.

C. In fact, homework may even be causing some kids to drop out of school.

D. A recent study by the State Department of Education asked high-school dropouts if any *one factor* had played a key role in causing them to leave school.

E. If teachers and parents can agree to less homework every night, then we'll have a happier, healthier student population, and more of them will be staying in school until graduation day.

Directions: Carefully read the passage below. It is part of a memoir written by a Mexican-American explorer and botanist (plant expert) named Ynes Mexia. She lived from 1870 to 1938. After you finish reading, answer each of the questions that follow by choosing the one *best* answer.

1   Most of us, I think, have felt the fascination of the Amazon region. So much have we heard of its rivers, its tropical beauty, its luxuriant forests . . . that the pictures drawn by our imagination are vivid and unique. This vision of the unspoiled wilderness drew me irresistibly. . . .

2   With some letters of introduction, a knowledge of Spanish, and a quantity of botanical-collecting equipment, I left San Francisco in October, 1929, taking a steamer that went through the [Panama] Canal and landed me in Rio de Janeiro. From there I went to the highlands of Brazil . . . and collected at various points there for a year and a half. Returning to Rio, I decided that if I wanted to become better acquainted with the South American continent the best way would be to make my way right across it. . . .

3   A comfortable motorship took me up the Brazilian coast to Pará, at the mouth of the Amazon, where the staff of the Goeldi Museum did much to assist me in my preparations. On August 28, 1931, with a truckload of equipment, I boarded the river-steamer *Victoria* and started up the famous river. Surely there was no roughing it on the steamer. Screened cabins, electric fans, ice . . ., as well as fresh meat. . . .

4   The river itself is a tawny* flood, looking more like an inland sea . . . than a river. Everywhere it is island-sown, and these islands divide it into *paranás,* or channels, each of which may be several miles wide. [Boats going up] the river follow these side channels, often bringing the boat sufficiently close to island-shore or mainland to enable one to see many interesting features. Every foot of [land] is heavily wooded, and these forests of the Lower Amazon are truly magnificent. . . .

5   The sixth day up the river brought us to the town of Óbydos, perched on low pink cliffs, a rare sight in this flattest of [places], and remarkable as one of only two points where both banks of the Amazon can be seen [without islands in between].

GO ON ▶

6   After leaving Óbydos the wild life became more abundant. Huge . . . caimans** slid off sand-banks as we chugged along. Numbers of the beautiful white aigret herons were outlined against the green of the forest bank, while flocks of chattering parrakeets flashed green and silver as they wheeled above the river. Everywhere are seen the dugout canoes, some holding half a dozen persons and carrying produce, and others, mere shells, with a single paddler. . . . Most numerous, of course, are the canoes around the little clearings, where the dwellers run out to watch the *Victoria* pass—a man or two, half a dozen ragged children, the . . . naked babies, and, in the background, the thatched† house built on stilts as a precaution against the floods.

7   Eight days up the river the map shows a [place called] "Santa Julia." It consisted of two forlorn-looking shacks standing apart. From the farther one [came] an official. He entered a canoe displaying the yellow-and-green Brazilian flag, and [called out to] the *Victoria*. When he came aboard I discovered that we were just entering the vast State of Amazonas, and needed his official permission. After another day or two, we arrived at Manaos. . . . It is the capital of the huge and little-explored State of Amazonas. Certainly a surprise, for this city, in the heart of what is generally considered a howling wilderness, is a very modern place, with wide, tree-shaded streets, electric trams, hospitals, splendid public buildings, and a beautiful opera-house of Italian marble topped with a gold-tiled dome. . . .

8   Time seems to have no meaning in this world of sky and water; but after twenty-two days of river life we reach the Rio Javary coming up from the south, which marks the boundary between Brazil and Peru. . . . Crossing the Javary we entered the territory of Peru. . . . This pathless wilderness [has never been surveyed], and Peru, Colombia, and Brazil each claimed this [until recently] . . . unwanted jungle. . . . Thus, in this obscure corner of the wilderness the three great countries meet—Brazil, Peru, and Colombia, with Ecuador clamoring for entrance—and this junction is [filled] with danger.

* tawny = of a warm, sandy color
** caimans = South American alligators
† thatched = roofing made of plant material (often straw)

GO ON ▶

1. What genre (type) of writing is this?

   A. novel

   B. short story

   C. autobiography

   D. biography

   E. editorial

2. Where was the starting point of the author's trip?

   A. the Panama Canal

   B. Rio de Janeiro

   C. San Francisco

   D. Mexico City

   E. Óbydos

3. For how long did Ynes Mexia collect plant specimens in the highlands of Brazil?

   A. 12 months

   B. 14 months

   C. 16 months

   D. 18 months

   E. 20 months

4. How did Ynes Mexia get from the highlands of Brazil to the mouth of the Amazon?

   A. She went overland by truck.

   B. She went by boat up the coast of Brazil.

   C. She traveled by canoe up the river.

   D. She went on the steamboat *Victoria*.

   E. She boarded a small train.

GO ON ▶

5. Which of the following statements best summarizes why the author was surprised when she arrived in Manaos?

   A. She expected to find a rough little village, but instead she found a modern city.

   B. She was amazed by all of the beautiful wildlife, like the herons and the caimans.

   C. She learned that there was more than one hospital in Manaos.

   D. She learned that Manaos was the capital of a huge state called Amazonas.

   E. The thatched houses were built on stilts in case of flooding.

6. For how long did Ynes Mexia travel up the Amazon River to reach the Rio Javary?

   A. 22 days

   B. 8 days

   C. 24 days

   D. 6 days

   E. 14 days

7. At the end of the fourth paragraph, what part of speech is the word *truly?*

   A. verb

   B. noun

   C. adjective

   D. adverb

   E. preposition

8. What part of speech is the word *chattering* in the sixth paragraph?

   A. verb

   B. adverb

   C. pronoun

   D. noun

   E. adjective

GO ON

9. The following statements are from the sixth paragraph on page 31. One statement tells the main idea of the paragraph; the rest are details. Which statement is the main idea?

A. Huge . . . caimans slid off sand-banks as we chugged along.

B. After leaving Óbydos the wildlife became more abundant.

C. Most numerous, of course, are the canoes around the little clearings, where the dwellers run out to watch the *Victoria* pass—a man or two, half a dozen ragged children, the . . . naked babies, and, in the background, the thatched house built on stilts as a precaution against the floods.

D. Numbers of the beautiful white aigret herons were outlined against the green of the forest bank, while flocks of chattering parrakeets flashed green and silver as they wheeled above the river.

E. Everywhere are seen the dugout canoes, some holding half a dozen persons and carrying produce, and others, mere shells, with a single paddler. . . .

10. Why did Ynes Mexia probably decide to go to the Amazon?

A. She loved nature in its unspoiled beauty and was willing to take risks to see more of it.

B. Although she loved to travel, she preferred to avoid the wilderness; however, the price of the trip to the Amazon was irresistible.

C. Having heard many stories about the capital city of Manaos, she decided to see it for herself.

D. She had heard many romantic stories about the Amazon region and hoped to meet her future husband there.

E. She knew how to speak Spanish and wanted to get more practice in order to become fluent.

STOP

Directions: The excerpt below comes from a British book that was written around the turn of the twentieth century. Published in 1901, *The Wouldbegoods* by E. Nesbit is about the Bastable family, who are on their summer vacation ("summer holiday") when this passage begins. Read the excerpt. Then answer each question that follows by choosing the *best* possible answer.

We were very pleased when Father said—

"I've asked Mr. Foulkes to send his children here for a week or two. You know—the kids who came at Christmas. You must be jolly to them, and see that they have a good time, don't you know."

We remembered them right enough—they were little pinky, frightened things, like white mice, with very bright eyes. They had not been to our house since Christmas, because Denis [Denny], the boy, had been ill. . . .

The train got in at 12:27. We all went to meet them. Afterwards I thought that was a mistake, because their aunt was with them, and she wore black with beady things and a tight bonnet, and she said, when we took our hats off—

"Who are you?" quite crossly.

We said, "We are the Bastables; we've come to meet Daisy and Denny."

The aunt is a very rude lady, and it made us sorry for Daisy and Denny when she said to them—

"*Are* these the children? Do you remember them?"

We weren't very tidy, perhaps, because we'd been playing brigands [bandits] in the shrubbery; and we knew we should have to wash for dinner as soon as we got back, anyhow. But still—

Denny said he thought he remembered us. But Daisy said, "Of course they are," and then looked as if she was going to cry. . . .

So then the aunt called a cab, and told the man where to drive, and put Daisy and Denny in, and then she said—

"You two little girls may go too, if you like, but you little boys must walk."

So the cab went off, and we were left. The aunt turned to us to say a few last words. We knew it would have been about brushing your hair and wearing gloves, so Oswald [the oldest Bastable child] said, "Good-bye," and turned haughtily* away, before she could begin, and so did the others. No one but that kind of black beady tight lady would say "little boys." . . .

When we got home we found all four of those who had ridden in the cab sitting in our sitting room . . . looking thoroughly washed, and our girls were asking polite questions and the others were saying "Yes" and "No," and "I don't know." We boys did not say anything. We stood at the window and looked out till the gong went for dinner. We felt it was going to be awful—and it was.

They said "Yes, please," and "No, thank-you"; and they ate very neatly, and always wiped their mouths before they drank, as well as after, and never spoke with them full.

And after dinner it got worse and worse. . . .

I don't think I was ever glad of bedtime before, but that time I was.

When they had gone to bed (Daisy had to have all her strings and buttons undone for her, Dora told me, though she is nearly ten, and Denny said he couldn't sleep without the gas [light] being left a little bit on) we held a council in the girls' room. We all sat on the bed—it is a mahogany fourposter with green curtains very good for tents . . ., and Oswald said—

"This is jolly** nice, isn't it?"

"They'll be better tomorrow," Alice said, "they're only shy."

Dicky said shy was all very well, but you needn't behave like a perfect idiot.

"They're frightened. You see we're all strange to them," Dora said.

"We're not wild beasts . . . we shan't eat them. What have they got to be frightened of?" Dicky said this.

Noel told us he thought they were an enchanted prince and princess who'd been turned into white rabbits, and their bodies had got changed back but not their insides.

But Oswald told him to dry up.

"It's no use making things up about them," he said. "The thing is: what are we going to *do?* We can't have our holidays spoiled by these sniveling† kids."

"No," Alice said, "but they can't possibly go on sniveling for ever. Perhaps they've got into the habit of it with that [awful] aunt. She's enough to make anyone snivel."

"All the same," said Oswald, "we jolly well aren't going to have another day like today. We must do something to rouse them from their sniveling. . . ."

"A booby trap," said H.O., "the first thing when they get up, and an apple-pie bed†† at night."

* haughtily = proudly, scornfully
** jolly = (1) happy (adjective); (2) very, certainly (adverb)
† sniveling = crying, whining
†† apple-pie bed = a bed that has been made up with a short bottom sheet, so that it is impossible to get into

GO ON ▶

1. What is the main purpose of this passage?

   A. to entertain
   B. to inform
   C. to persuade
   D. to give directions, to instruct
   E. to ask for something

2. Why do Daisy and Denny come to visit the Bastables?

   A. Daisy and Denny's aunt is an old friend of the Bastable family, and she has arranged it.
   B. Mr. Bastable has invited them because he is friendly with Daisy and Denny's father.
   C. They are going to be starting school with the Bastable children.
   D. It is nearly Christmas time, and they are coming to celebrate.
   E. Their aunt can no longer keep them with her, so the Bastables have taken them in.

3. According to clues in the text, how many Bastable children are there, not including the narrator?

   A. four
   B. three
   C. six
   D. seven
   E. five

4. All but one of the following statements are true about this story. Which one is *not* true?

   A. The Bastables have met Daisy and Denny before.
   B. The Bastables go to meet Daisy and Denny at the train.
   C. The narrator thinks that going to the train has been a mistake.
   D. Daisy and Denny's aunt is not very nice to the Bastables.
   E. Daisy and Denny are pleased to see the Bastables again.

5. Based on information in the text, how do Daisy and Denny probably feel about coming to visit?

   A. happy

   B. unhappy

   C. furious

   D. amused

   E. envious

6. Why does Oswald "turn haughtily away" from the aunt?

   A. He doesn't want her to lecture him about good manners.

   B. He is anxious to act like a grownup and please her.

   C. He has just heard someone calling his name.

   D. She has just hurt his feelings, and he is about to cry.

   E. His father has taught him to do this in front of a lady.

7. The narrator says, "We remembered them right enough—they were little pinky, frightened things, like white mice, with very bright eyes." What is this an example of?

   A. metaphor

   B. hyperbole

   C. irony

   D. simile

   E. alliteration

8. That night, when Oswald says, "This is jolly nice, isn't it?" he is speaking with _____.

   A. happiness

   B. irony

   C. a metaphor

   D. gratefulness

   E. relief

GO ON ▶

9. All of the following statements *except one* are true about the passage on pages 35 and 36. Which one of these statements is *not* true?

   A. H.O. suggests setting booby-traps for Daisy and Denny.

   B. Oswald says that they need to stop Daisy and Denny from "sniveling."

   C. Alice says that Daisy and Denny should take the next train back home.

   D. Noel says that Daisy and Denny are really an enchanted prince and princess.

   E. Dora says that Daisy and Denny must be frightened.

10. **Short-answer response:** Write a one-page response to these questions:

    • Do the Bastables become friends with Daisy and Denny?

    • What do you think will happen in the story to bring this about?

    As you write your predictions, be sure to use complete sentences. You should also use information from the reading passage to back up your thinking. You will need a separate sheet of paper on which to write your response.

SECTION 4

SECTION 4.1

Directions: The selection that follows is from a letter sent by Theodore Roosevelt to his children in 1898. At the time, Roosevelt was Assistant Secretary of the United States Navy. The United States had just declared war on Spain, and Roosevelt was in Florida organizing troops. Soon thereafter, he led his own regiment, called the Rough Riders, into battle in Cuba. Read the letter carefully. Then answer the questions that follow.

Camp at Tampa [Florida], May 6th, '98

Blessed Bunnies,

It has been a real holiday to have darling mother here. Yesterday I brought her out to the camp, and she saw it all—the men drilling, the tents in long company streets, the horses being taken to water, my little horse Texas, the colonel and the majors, and finally the mountain lion and the jolly little dog Cuba, who had several fights while she looked on. The mountain lion is not much more than a kitten as yet, but it is very cross and treacherous.

We were all, horses and men, four days and four nights on the [railroad] cars coming here from San Antonio, and were very tired and very dirty when we arrived. I was up almost all of each night, for it happened always to be at night when we took the horses out of the cars to feed and water them.

Mother stays at a big hotel about a mile from camp. There are nearly thirty-thousand troops here now, besides the sailors from the war-ships in the bay. At night the corridors and piazzas* are thronged with officers of the army and navy; the older ones fought in the great Civil War, a third of a century ago, and now they are all going to Cuba to war against the Spaniards. Most of them are in blue, but our rough-riders are in brown. Our camp is on a great flat, on sandy soil without a tree, though round about are pines and palmettos. It is very hot, indeed, but there are no mosquitoes. . . . A general was out to inspect us when we were drilling to-day.

* piazza = a terrace or square where people gather to chat and visit

GO ON ▶

1. Which of the following best describes the tone of this letter?

    A. angry and complaining

    B. sad and homesick

    C. affectionate and cheerful

    D. cool and polite

2. Not counting the soldiers who were on ships, how many troops were in Florida at the time of this letter?

    A. almost 30,000

    B. almost 20,000

    C. almost 40,000

    D. almost 10,000

3. Based on information in the letter, which of the following statements is most likely true about Roosevelt?

    A. He very much disliked military life.

    B. He was afraid of horses.

    C. He loved animals and children.

    D. He did not believe that Civil War veterans should fight in the war with Spain.

4. What color did the "rough-riders" wear?

    A. blue

    B. brown

    C. gray

    D. olive green

5. Who is "cross and treacherous," according to the letter?

    A. Mother

    B. the colonel

    C. the dog Cuba

    D. the little mountain lion

© 2003 J. Weston Walch, Publisher   *Test Time! Critical Reading*

Directions: Read the passage below. Then answer the questions that follow.

1   Gemstones are very special kinds of stones or minerals. A gemstone has certain qualities that make it worth cutting, then polishing, finally to become a piece of jewelry or an ornament. The most popular and durable gemstones—like diamonds, rubies, emeralds, and sapphires—all come from the mineral group.

2   Are *all* minerals gemstones? No; actually, gemstones are relatively rare. In fact, in addition to their beauty, it is this rarity that makes gems so valuable— and expensive. Other factors affecting the value of a gemstone include its size, color, brilliance, and clarity.

3   Gemstones, in all their rainbow of colors, can come from a variety of different rock and mineral formations. Emeralds, for example, are igneous gems; rubies and sapphires are metamorphic in nature; opals are sedimentary formations. Diamonds, known for their extreme hardness and brilliance, are formed from pure carbon. They are formed in volcanic areas deep below the surface of the earth.

4   In short, no matter what layer of the earth they come from, gemstones are certainly the loveliest creations in nature.

1. What is the meaning of the word *durable* in the first paragraph?

   A. able to do many things

   B. long-lasting

   C. expensive

   D. colorful

GO ON

2. What is the meaning of the word *clarity* in the second paragraph?

   A. the quality of being clear

   B. the hardness of a substance

   C. high price

   D. simplicity of design

3. What part of speech is the word *extreme* in the third paragraph?

   A. adverb

   B. verb

   C. adjective

   D. noun

4. Three of the statements that follow are facts from this reading passage. One statement is an opinion. Which one is the opinion?

   A. Other factors affecting the value of a gemstone include its size, color, brilliance, and clarity.

   B. Gemstones can come from a variety of different rock and mineral formations.

   C. Emeralds, for example, are igneous gems; rubies and sapphires are metamorphic in nature; opals are sedimentary formations.

   D. In short, no matter what layer of the earth they come from, gemstones are certainly the loveliest creations in nature.

© 2003 J. Weston Walch, Publisher

Directions: Study the temperature table below. Then answer each of the questions that follow by selecting the *best* possible choice.

Weather Around the World

September 30

	High	Low			High	Low			High	Low	
Athens	74	57	s	Frankfurt	61	44	s	New Delhi	98	67	s
Auckland	61	47	pc	Geneva	62	45	pc	Oslo	59	51	sh
Barbados	87	78	pc	Hong Kong	80	74	r	Paris	67	49	s
Beijing	81	56	s	Jerusalem	93	64	s	Rome	64	47	pc
Berlin	59	49	pc	London	74	55	pc	São Paulo	82	65	s
Bermuda	87	77	pc	Madrid	75	54	c	Singapore	86	77	c
Bogota	71	46	pc	Mexico City	79	54	pc	Sydney	68	44	s
Cairo	102	72	s	Moscow	47	43	r	Taipei	80	69	sh
Dublin	66	57	c	Nairobi	82	52	pc	Tokyo	75	74	t
								Vancouver	50	38	pc

KEY: s = sunny; pc = partly cloudy; c = cloudy; r = rain; sh = showers; t = thunderstorms; sn = snow; i = ice

1. Which city had the highest temperature on September 30?

    A. Jerusalem

    B. New Delhi

    C. Nairobi

    D. Cairo

2. Which city had the lowest temperature?

    A. Frankfurt

    B. Moscow

    C. Sydney

    D. Vancouver

GO ON ▶

3. Which of the following cities had the clearest skies?

   A. Paris

   B. Geneva

   C. Moscow

   D. Singapore

4. Which of the following cities experienced thunderstorms?

   A. Tokyo

   B. Bogota

   C. Hong Kong

   D. Oslo

5. Each of the following pairs of cities *except one* had weather that was quite similar on September 30. Which pair of cities had weather that was *not* similar?

   A. Frankfurt and Paris

   B. Taipei and Oslo

   C. Barbados and Bermuda

   D. London and Mexico City

SECTION 1.1 (Fiction: Excerpt from *My Antonia*)

1. A
2. C
3. B
4. B
5. D

SECTION 1.2 (Informational Text: Flag Etiquette)

1. D
2. A
3. B
4. C
5. A

SECTION 1.3 (Informational Text: Frescoes)

1. C
2. A
3. A
4. C
5. D

SECTION 2.1 (Biography: Rachel Carson)

1. D   6. A
2. B   7. A
3. C   8. D
4. B   9. C
5. D   10. C

SECTION 2.2 (Poem: "The Pines")

1. A
2. D
3. D
4. C
5. Answers will vary. Possible responses might include that the first stanza creates a "grim," slightly threatening mood, where the world seems "gray"; the second stanza is warmer-hearted and more hopeful; the fourth stanza may again elicit feelings of discouragement and isolation; the final stanza ends on an upbeat note, eliciting feelings of inspiration and fellowship.

SECTION 2.3 (Poem: "A Gust of Fall Wind")

1. B
2. A
3. A
4. C
5. Answers will vary, but should include as many of the following as possible: *Theme:* "The Pines" stresses human solidarity in times of trouble or "storm"; "A Gust of Fall Wind" stresses human isolation and destruction. *Tone:* "The Pines" is serious yet uplifting, ending on a reassuring, hopeful note; "A Gust of Fall

Wind" is bleak and despairing. *Type of Verse:* "The Pines" is in a traditional rhyming meter, with five stanzas of three lines each; "A Gust of Fall Wind" is in free verse, and it is much shorter, with just four lines. *Literary Devices:* "The Pines" primarily uses alliteration, personification, and simile; "A Gust of Fall Wind" primarily uses repetition and metaphor. Students might also mention that "The Pines" is somewhat more self-explanatory and direct, while "A Gust of Fall Wind" requires the reader to make a mental leap from the metaphorical grasshopper to a human being, and from there to the human condition in general.

SECTION 3.1 (Editorial: Homework)

1. E
2. D
3. A
4. C
5. B
6. E

SECTION 3.2 (Autobiography: Ynes Mexia)

1. C
2. C
3. D
4. B
5. A
6. A
7. D
8. E
9. B
10. A

SECTION 3.3 (Fiction: *The Wouldbegoods* by E. Nesbit)

1. A
2. B
3. C
4. E

5. B
6. A
7. D
8. B
9. C
10. Answers will vary. Students should make reasonable predictions, using information from the story to back up their ideas.

SECTION 4.1 (Letter: Theodore Roosevelt from Camp at Tampa)

1. C
2. A
3. C
4. B
5. D

SECTION 4.2 (Informational Text: Gemstones)

1. B
2. A
3. C
4. D

SECTION 4.3 (Table: Weather Around the World)

1. D
2. D
3. A
4. A
5. B